The Art of Regency

This book belongs to:

_____

COLORING GRAND ESTATES, PORTRAITS, AND INTERIORS

© 2023
ISBN 979-8-9890022-4-5

Designed by Aidyrose Books, Aidyrose LLC

Made in the USA

For Isabele

Made in the USA
Las Vegas, NV
30 January 2024